Printed and Published in Great Britain by D. C. THOMSON & CO., LTD.,
185 Fleet Street, London, EC4A 2HS.   © D. C. THOMSON & CO., LTD., 1986
ISBN 0 85116 359 9

HAVE A SMASHING TIME WITH

The SMASHER

WATCH THIS, FOLKS!

YIPPEE! A DIRECT HIT!

SMASH!

GOTCHA!

OO-ER!

BREAKING BOTTLES IS A DANGEROUS GAME — I'LL LET YOU OFF ON ONE CONDITION . . .

. . . WILL YOU HELP OUT AT A STALL AT THE POLICE FETE?

OKAY!

HMM! I WONDER IF I'LL BE AT THE "KNOCKING DOWN THE GOALKEEPER" STALL?

DESPERATE DAN

See the pictures below! Has Dan become a TV star? Read on and find out what he's up to!

RUB!
SHARPEN!

VET

The contest begins —

— AND TO OPEN OUR CONTEST, SIDNEY GEORDIE WILL PLAY BIG JOCK AT LUDO!

SHAKE, PAL!

VERY SPORTING! SURE I WILL!

HAPPY LANDINGS! HA-HA!

YAHOO!

WHAT ON EARTH!

AARGH!

OOF!

GURR! I SAID LUDO NOT JUDO!

SO SORRY! MY MISTAKE! TEE-HEE!

OOH!

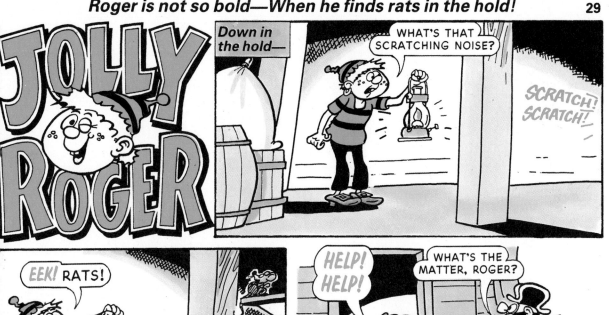

Mitch AND HIS MUMMY

ICARUS MADE WINGS FROM FEATHERS AND WAS ABLE TO FLY, MITCH!

YES! BUT HE FLEW TOO CLOSE TO THE SUN AND THE WAX HOLDING HIS FEATHERS MELTED!

I'M OFF TO MAKE MYSELF A SET OF WINGS!

WORKSHOP

Soon— CAREFUL, MUMMY! REMEMBER WHAT HAPPENED TO ICARUS!

DON'T WORRY, MITCH! IT'S NOT SUNNY TODAY!

Oh-oh! The glue isn't dry yet.

WE HAVE LIFT-OFF!

But then— ERK! MY WING TIPS HAVE STUCK TOGETHER!

STUCK

GOING DOWN! GULP!

GOOD! A SOFT LANDING!

NEWSAGENTS

Creepy droned on —

ROME IS ALSO NOTED FOR ITS BEAUTIFUL FOUNTAINS, AS THIS PICTURE SHOWS.

And on!

AND HERE'S ANOTHER HISTORICAL BUILDING! SUCH CULTURE! SUCH ART!

SUCH A BORING OLD GOAT!

YAWN!

BUT I DON'T WANT TO HOG THE SHOW. DID ANY OF YOU BOYS TAKE INTERESTING SLIDES ON YOUR HOLIDAYS?

YES, SIR! ME, SIR!

I WAS AT BRIGHTSEA, AND I'VE BROUGHT MY SLIDES ALONG WITH ME!

FASCINATING! DO LET US SEE THEM!

THIS SLIDE SHOWS HOW TO WANGLE YOUR WAY TO THE FRONT OF AN ICE CREAM QUEUE.

ICE CREAM

NO! I DON'T THINK WE SHOULD SEE ANY MORE OF THIS!

IT'S ABOUT TIME YOU BOYS LEARNED A BIT ABOUT CULTURE — AND I'VE GOT AN IDEA!

And so Creepy had a talk with the Headmaster —

BUILDING A FOUNTAIN IN HONOUR OF OUR SCHOOL'S FOUNDER? THAT'S A SPLENDID IDEA, CREEP! GO AHEAD!

Next morning, a lorry pulled up at Greytowers gates —

WE'VE COME TO BUILD THE FOUNTAIN, GUV'NOR!

LANDSCAPE GARDENING

DO COME IN! DON'T WORRY ABOUT THE LABOURING WORK — THE BOYS WILL DO THAT!

So a very unhappy Winker and his pals were put to work, digging the foundations for the fountain —

BAH! ROTTEN OLD CREEPY! I'LL FIX HIM FOR THIS!

PHEW!

Later —

HMM! I THINK I'VE AN IDEA TO FIX CREEPY!

TELL ME, HOW DO THE FOUNTAIN'S WATER NOZZLES WORK?

OH, THAT'S EASY . . .

The fountain neared completion —

ALMOST DONE! JUST NEEDS A LICK OF PAINT NOW!

By mid-afternoon it was completed. But as the workmen took a tea-break, Winker quietly sneaked up to the fountain —

NOW TO MAKE A FEW ADJUSTMENTS!

Shortly —

ALL FINISHED! WONDERFUL! NOW WE CAN INVITE THE SCHOOL GOVERNORS TO THE GRAND SWITCHING-ON CEREMONY!

Next day, the Governors arrived —

WELCOME, SIR, MADAM! DO COME IN!

HELLO, CREEP.

GREYTOWERS SCHOOL FOUNTAIN DAY

I WONDER, SIR, IF YOU WOULD DO US THE HONOUR OF SWITCHING ON OUR NEW FOUNTAIN?

DELIGHTED TO OBLIGE!

IT GIVES ME GREAT PLEASURE TO TURN ON THIS SPLENDID FOUNTAIN!

There was water everywhere! Crafty Winker had tricked Creepy again, and got a great slide photograph into the bargain!

HAM and EGGHEAD

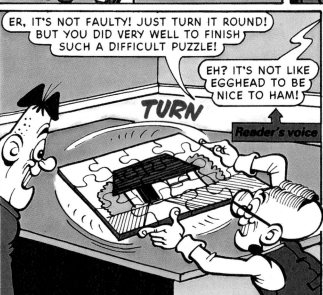

THE SMASHER

GLASSWARE DEPARTMENT

THIS IS THE DEPARTMENT I WANT TO SEE, SMASHER!

HALT!

?
?

READ THAT!

OH, DEAR!

ALL CUSTOMERS ARE WELCOME- EXCEPT SMASHER

I'LL TAKE A LOOK IN HERE WHILE MUM'S IN THE GLASSWARE DEPARTMENT!

TOY DEPT →

HMM! A TOY CANNON — I MUST HAVE A GO!

TOYS

OOPS!

OOYAH!

BIFF!

IT WAS A BOY WITH SPIKY BLACK HAIR!

GURR! I KNOW THE RASCAL!

ext—

THIS SHOULD CAUSE SOME EXCITEMENT—

TOY

WIND!

HO-HO!

HELP!

AARGH!

OH, NO! THAT EAGLE THINKS OUR BALLOON IS A REAL SAUSAGE!

SCREECH!

PECK!

ZOOOOM!

BLAM!

ARE THOSE PEOPLE GATE-CRASHING YOUR PARTY, MR MAYOR?

NO! I THINK THEY'RE JUST CRASHING!

FSSSSSS!

CRASH!

THE SHERIFF AND DAN ARE IN NO FIT STATE TO STOP ME NOW!

STICK 'EM UP! HAND OVER YOUR WALLETS, YOUR JEWELLERY AND YOUR DOLLY MIXTURES!

IT'S BACK-PACK JACK! WE'D BETTER DO WHAT HE SAYS!

HA-HA! QUITE RIGHT, MO! I LET THE KIDS BORROW SOME OF MY ANIMALS!

IT'S MR DOBSON, THE ZOO KEEPER!

YOU SEE, I WANTED TO KNOW HOW GOOD YOU WERE AT HANDLING WILD ANIMALS, 'COS I MIGHT WANT YOU TO BABYSIT FOR ME!

WELL, I'VE PROVED I CAN HANDLE ANY WILD ANIMAL! WHAT DO YOU WANT ME TO LOOK AFTER? A CROCODILE? A TIGER?

NO! LET ME INTRODUCE YOU TO—

AARGH! NOT THAT!

IT'S MR DOBSON'S SON, RUPERT! HE REALLY IS A WILD ANIMAL!

GOO! GOO! LET'S PLAY AT COWBOYS AND INDIANS!

This is Eddie Potter, an ordinary schoolboy. In fact he's the ONLY ordinary schoolboy at a very weird school!

THE SCHOOL'S HAVING A JUMBLE SALE TODAY, SO WE'RE ALL BRINGING ALONG OLD TOYS TO SELL ON THE STALLS!

SCHOOL

HI, VINCE, WHAT HAVE YOU GOT THERE?

HELLO, EDDIE!

OH, SOME OF MY OLD CLOCKWORK CARS! *HAW-HAW!*

WHIRR!

GASP! A HEARSE!

Then—

ER... WHAT HAVE YOU BROUGHT, HAIRY?

JUST SOME OLD CHAINS AND COBWEBS, EDDIE!

CLANK! CLANK!

OO... ER!

EXCELLENT! THE STALLS ARE FILLING UP WELL!

I'VE BROUGHT SOME COMBS!

HO-HO! WOLF MUST HAVE DOZENS OF THOSE FOR HIS HAIRY FACE.

THUD!

Soon—

ONLY ONE OWNER

USED SHROUDS

HEE-HEE! NO ONE WILL BUY THAT LOAD OF RUBBISH!

Just then—

SCREECH!

EH? WHO'S THIS?

GREAT! I'LL BUY MOST OF THIS STUFF!

EH?

WELL, ALL SOLD — EXCEPT YOUR ODD-LOOKING TOYS, EDDIE!

BUT WHO WAS HE?

A FILM MAKER! HE'S MAKING A "HORROR FILM", AND HE SAID THESE THINGS WERE PERFECT PROPS!

SPINE CHILLER PRODUCTIONS

HO-HO!

HAM and EGGHEAD

HAM

HELLO, FOLKS! MY NAME IS DEREK DUMMY!

I'M THE BRAINIEST GUY IN THIS STORY!

THERE'S HAM, MY SILLY BILLY PAL. I WONDER WHAT HE'S DOING WITH A BOOK!

I'M GOING TO BE A VENTRILOQUIST! I HAVE A DUMMY TOO, EGGHEAD!

HOW TO THROW YOUR VOICE

HAM'S HOUSE

WELL, LET ME HEAR YOU THROW YOUR VOICE!

BROOM CUPBOARD

BUMP!

HELP! LET ME OUT!

THAT'S VERY GOOD!

BROOM CUPBOARD

R, SORRY FOR SHUTTING YOU IN THE CUPBOARD, DAD!

CLUMSY FOOL!

SO, IT WASN'T AM THROWING HIS VOICE AT ALL!

THIS IS MY DUMMY! I'LL SHOW YOU WHAT I CAN DO!

NOW, YOU TURN THE POLE TO MOVE THE HEAD, AND PULL A WIRE TO OPEN AND SHUT ITS MOUTH...

WELL GO ON THEN!

THE MONSTERS OF CORRIE ISLAND

STEVE and Vicky Bennett were trapped! Towering above them, and poised to attack, was a giant rat with fangs as big as those of a killer shark! And behind the youngsters was a sheer drop to the rocky shore far below! How could they possibly escape?

But our story starts earlier that day on the tiny Corrie Island off the Scottish coast. Steve and Vicky were living there with their father, Professor Bennett, while he carried out scientific experiments on plants and vegetables.

THAT GIANT CARROT AND ONION WILL MAKE AN AMAZING PICTURE, DAD!

YES! MY LATEST BATCH OF SUPER-FERTILISER IS THE BEST YET!

SEE YOU LATER, DAD! WE'RE OFF TO PHOTOGRAPH WILD BIRDS AT THE CLIFFS! WE'LL TAKE PATCHES ALONG!

ALL RIGHT, BUT BE CAREFUL!

I'VE NEVER SEEN SO MANY BIRDS IN MY LIFE!

WE'RE BOUND TO GET LOTS OF GREAT PHOTOGRAPHS TODAY!

Meanwhile, a small boat had just arrived at Corrie Island's tiny jetty.

THE BOSS WANTS US TO CHECK OUT THIS ISLAND TO SEE IF IT'S A SAFE PLACE TO HIDE OUR SMUGGLED GOODS!

HEY! THERE'S SOMEONE ON THE ISLAND! HE COULD RUIN OUR PLANS!

WE'D BETTER TAKE HIM OUT TO THE YACHT. THE BOSS WILL KNOW WHAT TO DO WITH HIM!

HANDLE WITH CARE

But as the smugglers sneaked towards the professor . . .

EH? WHAT DO YOU WANT?

SWEET DREAMS, BUDDY!

RIGHT! LET'S SEE WHAT THE BOSS HAS TO SAY ABOUT THIS GUY!

But the thugs had no idea the flask Professor Bennett had been holding contained his super-fertiliser.

And this powerful liquid was now spilling on to the ground.

TELL THE BOSS WE HAVE A VISITOR FOR HIM!

Meanwhile on the cliff-top—

HELP! LOOK, STEVE!

OH, NO! IT'S . . . IT'S HORRIBLE!

Steve and Vicky were horrified to discover that the professor's super-fertiliser didn't only make vegetables grow gigantic.

IT'S A RAT! BUT IT'S HUGE!

AND WE'RE TRAPPED ON THE CLIFF-TOP!

GET BACK, YOU BRUTE!

Just when it looked as if Steve and Vicky were goners . . .

THAT BIRD'S EVEN BIGGER THAN THE RAT! THIS IS INCREDIBLE!

. . . a giant hawk swooped down on its chosen prey! The rat wasn't the only creature on Corrie Island to have been effected by the super-fertiliser.

But the rat had no intention of giving up without a fight and dug its sharp teeth into the hawk's leg!

The bird's mighty talons lost their grip and the rat dropped like a stone towards the smugglers' yacht in the water far below!

A GIANT RAT! I DON'T BELIEVE IT!

OH, NO! IT'S CLIMBING ON BOARD!

ABANDON SHIP!

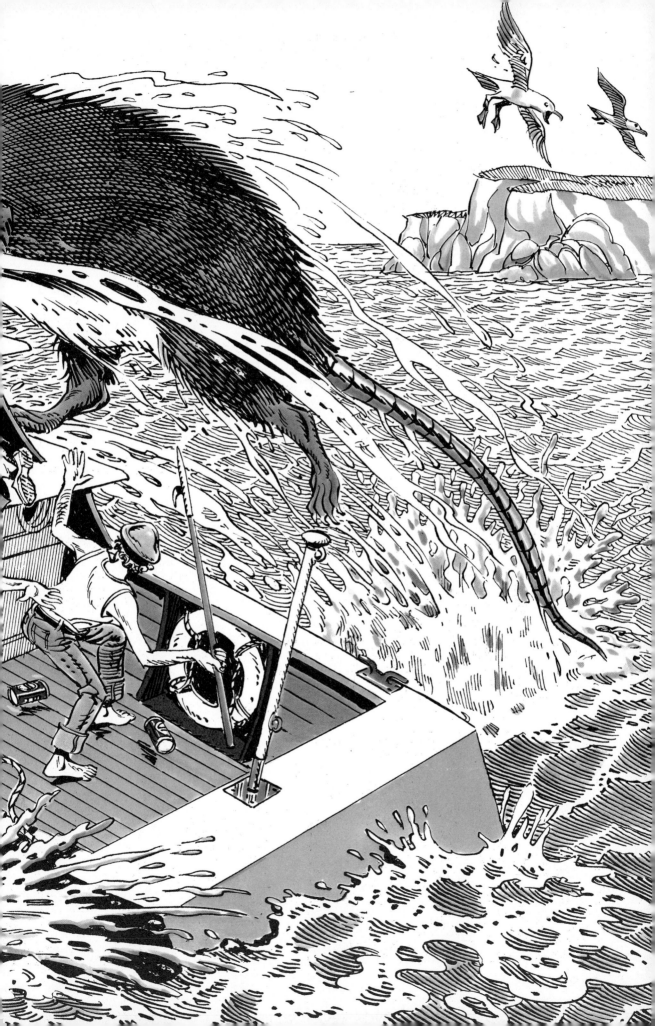

Steve and Vicky saw everything from the cliff-top.

LOOK! IT'S DAD!

AND THOSE THUGS ARE AFTER HIM!

ONE OF THEM HAS A GUN!

THEY HAVEN'T SPOTTED US YET, STEVE! WHAT SHOULD WE DO?

COME ON! WE CAN RADIO FOR HELP FROM DAD'S LAB!

...THIS IS CORRIE ISLAND CALLING THE COASTGUARDS...

And then—

THE COASTGUARDS SHOULD BE HERE SOON! WE'D BETTER HEAD BACK TO THE BEACH!

Suddenly—

A GIANT WEASEL! STAY BACK, VICKY!

The beast swung round, blocking Steve and Vicky's escape route.

IT'S NO USE! THIS BRANCH WON'T KEEP IT AT BAY FOR LONG!

But just then—

IT'S PATCHES!

AND HE'S GROWN TOO!

THAT-A-BOY, PATCHES!

PATCHES IS SEEING OFF THAT WEASEL! LET'S GET DOWN TO THE BEACH!

Professor Bennett explained to the astonished coastguards that his experiments had caused Patches' giant size.

A few days later —

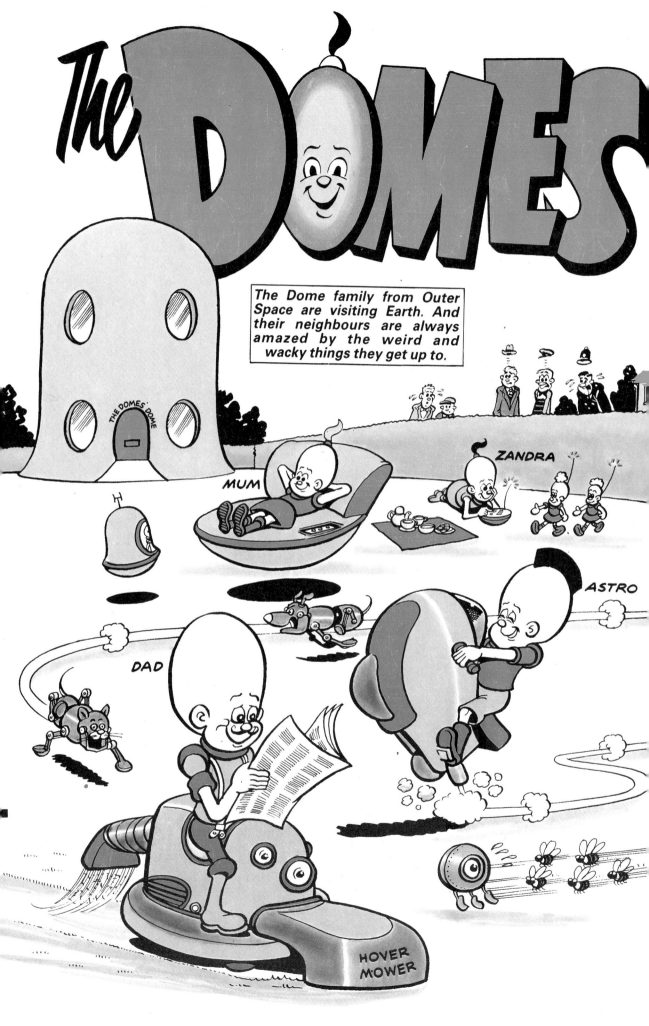

The JOCKS and the GEORDIES

I AM YOUR MASTER!

YOU-ARE-MY-MASTER!

Our tale begins one morning—

THIS LOOKS LIKE AN INTERESTING BOOK!

SECOND-HAND BOOKS CHEAP

ALL ABOUT HYPNOTISM

IT GIVES ME AN IDEA HOW WE CAN PLAY SOME TRICKS ON THE JOCKS.

OH, GOODY

ALL ABOUT HYPNOTISM

ALL ABOUT HYPNOTISM

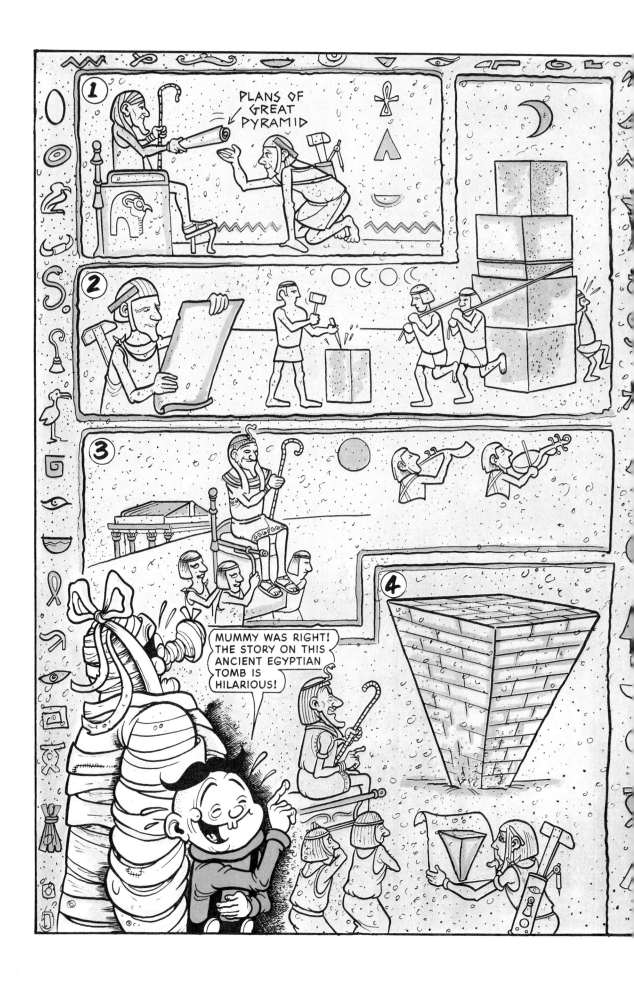

DESPERATE DAN

But —

ER — IT'S FAR TOO BIG! I RECKON I DON'T KNOW THE DIFFERENCE BETWEEN CENTIMETRES AND METRES!

BLUSH!

PATTERN

YOU BIG GALOOT!

CUDDLY TOY STUFFING :— ONE DOLLAR PER BAG

STUFFING

SHUCKS! I'D BE BROKE LONG BEFORE I'D FILLED THIS BEAR FULL OF STUFFING!

HMM! I WONDER!

SCRAP YARD

LOADING BAY

I'LL GRATE UP THESE OLD TYRES AND FILL THE BEAR WITH RUBBER CHIPS INSTEAD!

HARRY AND HIS HIPPO

PHOTOGRAPHIC COMPETITION
PRIZES FOR BEST PHOTOGRAPHS SHOWN

LET'S ENTER FOR THAT!

I'LL PHOTOGRAPH YOU IN A FANCY POSE, HIPPO!

COULD YOU STAND LIKE THAT?

EASY!

CREAK!

HOLD IT!

BULLY BEEF and CHIPS

in "IT'S A FAIR COP"

The PUDDLEWICK PLAYGROUP

PART 4

THE SMASHER

I'M LEARNING TO PLAY THE BUGLE!

TUM-TE-TUM

TIP-TOE

BLARE!

YOW!

JUST KEEPING UP WITH MY BUGLE LESSONS, DAD — PRACTICE MAKES PERFECT!

YES! A PERFECT PEST!

Presently—

OLD SOLDIERS' REST HOME

HERE'S A CHANCE FOR FUN!

QUICK! TIME TO GET ON PARADE, LADS!

BLARE!

AT EASE, MEN! IT'S ONLY ME!

GRR!

BAH!

HUH!

Farther on—

HEH-HEH! MORE FUN COMING UP!